Spelling Star

C000112245

Contents

unit 1

Long vowel phonemes: ae and ee

🔑 Key idea

All words have vowels. Some words have only one vowel. Other words have more than one vowel. Two or more vowels in a word *usually* make a long vowel sound.

cap

cape

Look what happens to **cap** when we add an **e** to the end.

This word has two vowels. Can you hear the long vowel sound?

Read these **ae** words.
Can you hear the **ae** sounds?

pail   whale   great   eight   day   tape

Now read these **ee** words.
Can you hear the **ee** sounds?

sea   be   bee   meat   theme   bean

!

ALERT
Can you hear the long vowel phoneme in these words?
be   me   he
she   we

Try it out!

Find and write *ae* and *ee* words. The first one has been done to help you. There are ten more words to find.

(1 mark for each correct answer)

1 It was great fun at Ravi's wizard theme party. *(great, theme)*
2 A whale is a big animal that lives in the sea.
3 Jack will be eight tomorrow.
4 I like to have bean and meat stew for dinner.
5 My sister listens to her tape all day long.
6 The bee is on the rim of the pail.

Keep practising!

Write the missing letters. Choose from the words in the box.

(1 mark for each correct answer)

weigh	whey	maid	made	break
week	weak	scene	seen	brake

1 Little Miss Muffet ate curds and w_ _ _ .

2 There are 7 days in a w_ _ _ .

3 Have you s_ _ _ the wizard doing magic tricks?

4 You w_ _ _ _ the flour to make a cake.

5 I use the b_ _ _ _ on my bike to stop.

6 A baby is not strong, it is w_ _ _ .

7 The m_ _ _ did not mean to b_ _ _ _ the dish.

8 I m_ _ _ a model of a woodland s_ _ _ _ at school.

Take up the challenge!

1 **Write the word for each picture in your book.**

   (1 mark for each correct answer)

2 **Choose four of the words. Write a sentence for each word in your book.** *(1 mark for each sentence)*

unit 2
Long vowel phonemes: ie, oe and ue

🔑 Key idea

All words have vowels. Some words have only one vowel. Other words have more than one vowel. Two or more vowels in a word *usually* make a long vowel sound.

Read Pirate Pete's puzzle. How many **ie** words can you find?

I spy with my little eye, something beginning with f ... fly!

Read these **ie** words. Can you hear the **ie** sounds?

    I   sky   hide   writes

Now read these **oe** words. Can you hear the **oe** sounds?

    so   toe   dough   window

Last of all, read these **ue** words. Can you hear the **ue** sounds?

    blue   moon   view   use

!

ALERT
Here are some exceptions to the rule!
fight   only   to

Try it out! •

Find and write *ie*, *oe* and *ue* words. The first one has been done for you. There are ten more words to find. *(1 mark for each correct answer)*

1 The view from the top of the hill was so amazing. *(view, so)*

2 The moon shone in the sky.

3 I play hide and seek with Mum.

4 Dad always writes with blue ink.

5 We often use flour and water to make dough.

6 Dad painted the window frame yellow.

4

Keep practising!

Write the missing letters. Choose from the words in the box.

(1 mark for each correct answer)

blue	blew	so	sow	roll
sight	site	road	rode	role

1 Grandad wears glasses because his s_ _ _ _ is not very good now.

2 The farmer has to s_ _ the seeds in spring.

3 It is dangerous to play near a building s_ _ _ .

4 Mum baked a big bread r_ _ _ .

5 I had s_ many books I didn't know which one to read first.

6 Ravi took the r_ _ _ of king in our school play.

7 Tess b_ _ _ out the b_ _ _ candles.

8 Jasmine r_ _ _ the horse along the r_ _ _ .

Take up the challenge!

1 **Write the word in your book.** *(1.5 marks for each correct answer)*

2 **Write a sentence for each word in your book.**

(1 mark for each sentence)

5

unit 3
Vowel phonemes: oo (short) and ow

 **Key idea**

A phoneme is the smallest unit of sound in a word. A phoneme can have one, two, three or four letters in it, for example, p**u**t, g**oo**d, w**ould**, b**ough**.

Read the poem. Look for the words with **oo** or **ow** sounds.

When Pete looked in his kitchen,
He saw a mouse running around.
He stood on a chair and shuddered.
"Get out of my house," he growled.

But the animal took no notice.
"It's no good," said Pete with a sigh.
"I wish it would go away now.
I'll give it a push and say 'bye'!"

Oh no! A mouse in the house!

Try it out! •

Write the words you found in the poem under the right heading. The first two have been done for you. There are ten more to find.

(1 mark for each correct answer)

oo	ow
looked	mouse

Choose the correct word to complete the sentences. *(1 mark for each correct answer)*

1   The mouse lived in the *farmhouse/greenhouse* kitchen.
2   The man chopped the *wood/would* with an axe.
3   Jim liked to climb the oak tree and sit on a *bough/bow*.
4   We had to *push/hook* the clothes into the case.
5   The servant had to *bow/bough* to the king.
6   The man hung his coat on the *push/hook*.
7   The *town/cowboy* rode his horse into *town/pound*.
8   We had to *bow/count* all the *pound/bough* coins.

Take up the challenge! ●

1   **Write the words in your book. Choose the right letters from the box.** *(1 mark for each correct answer)*

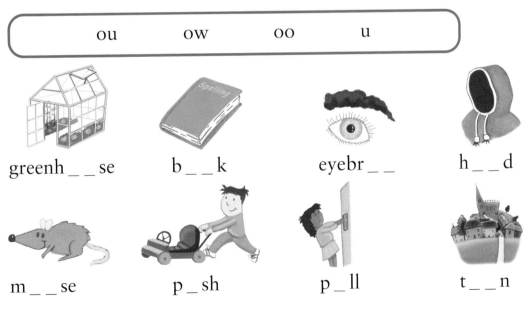

| ou | ow | oo | u |

greenh _ _ se   b _ _ k   eyebr _ _   h _ _ d

m _ _ se   p _ sh   p _ ll   t _ _ n

2   **Choose two of the words. Write a sentence for each word in your book.** *(1 mark for each sentence)*

Vowel phonemes:
ar and oy

 **Key idea**

Vowel phonemes can appear at the beginning, middle or end of a word, for example, **ar**m, m**ar**ket, c**ar**.

Remember that **oi** usually appears at the start or in the middle of a word but **oy** usually appears at the end of a word.

Look at the picture.

!

ALERT

Here are some exceptions to the rule:
r**oy**al l**oy**al

Shark ahoy!

Try it out! •

Write the right word for each number in the picture. The first one has been done for you. Choose from the words in the box.

(1 mark for each correct answer)

shark	coins	car	palm	chart	guitar
boy	buoy	oil	dart	soil	

1 guitar   4 _____   7 _____   10 _____

2 _____   5 _____   8 _____   11 _____

3 _____   6 _____   9 _____

8

Read the clues and write the word. Choose from the words
in the box. *(1 mark for each correct answer)*

art	marmalade	boil	alarm	royal
annoy	dark	march	card	loyal

1 You do this to water to make a drink of tea.

2 Younger sisters often do this to older sisters!

3 You might spread this on your toast for breakfast.

4 One of these might stop a burglar breaking in.

5 Some people are scared of this.

6 Soldiers do this when they are on parade.

7 On your birthday you might get one of these.

8 A faithful dog is called this.

9 You are this if you are a king or queen.

10 You draw and paint in this lesson.

Take up the challenge! •

1 **Write the word in your book.** *(1 mark for each correct answer)*

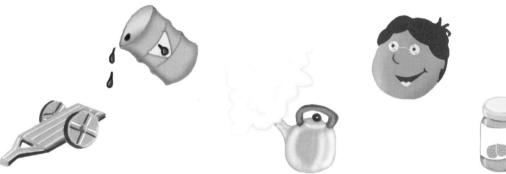

2 **Choose four of the words. Write a sentence for each word.**

   (1 mark for each sentence)

unit 5 — Plurals: adding s or es

 **Key idea**

A singular word refers to one thing. A plural word refers to more than one thing. You can make the plural of most words by adding **s**.

Read these plural words. Can you see the **s** at the end of each word?

ships   rats   bags   balloons   boys   cars

Most words ending in **o** are made into the plural by adding **s**. Read these plural words:

solos   pianos   banjos
logos   eskimos   igloos

> **!**
> **ALERT**
> Here are some exceptions to the rule!
> potatoes   tomatoes   echoes
> Some words ending in o can be made into the plural by adding s or es.
> flamingos
> flamingoes

Try it out! • • • • • • • • • • • • • • • •

Find and write the plural words. The first one has been done for you. There are ten more words to find. *(1 mark for each correct answer)*

1 The rats left the sinking ships. *(rats, ships)*
2 The plastic bags had the shop's logos on them.
3 The boys played their banjos very well.
4 Some eskimos live in igloos.
5 Three of the solos were performed on pianos at the concert.
6 Fred tied balloons to all the wedding cars!

1 **Write the right word. Choose from these words.**

(1 mark for each correct answer)

boys/buoys

planks/plants

knights/nights

sails/sales

boys/buoys

flowers/flours

2 **Put these words into sentences.** *(1 mark for each sentence)*

nights   planks   sales   flowers

**Use the letters to make a plural word. Remember each of these
plural words will end in *s*!** *(1 mark for each correct answer)*

1 pcus	4 toofbllas	7 rjas	9 keymons
2 thas	5 hscolos	8 oonms	10 weetss
3 rcas	6 enps		

unit 6

Past tense: –ed endings

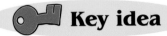 **Key idea**

A verb is a doing word. You can put many verbs into the past tense by adding **–ed** to the end of the word.

*Today I jump.
Yesterday I jumped.*

Here are some exceptions to the rule! You double the final consonant before adding **–ed** to some verbs.

stop = stopped   dim = dimmed
hop = hopped   dip = dipped

Try it out! . . . .

1 **Add –ed to these verbs.** *(1 mark for each correct answer)*

   want   need   pull   call   play

   Read the words you have made aloud.
   The –ed endings in these words say **d**.

2 **Now add –ed to these verbs.** *(1 mark for each correct answer)*

   look   push   walk   cross   lock

   Read aloud the words you have made.
   The –ed endings in these words say **t**.

Keep practising!

Write the word in your book. Choose from the words in the box.

(1 mark for each correct answer)

waited	chased	squeaked	kicked	shopped
dropped	cracked	counted	danced	dived

1

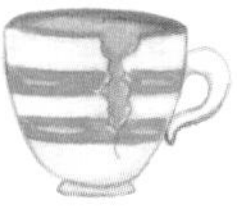

2

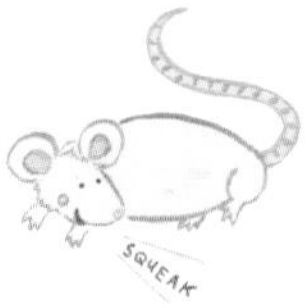

3

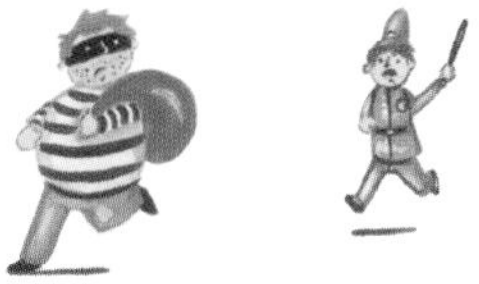

4

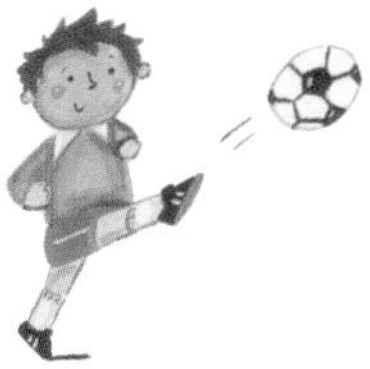

5

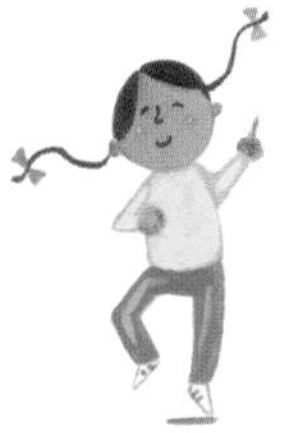

6

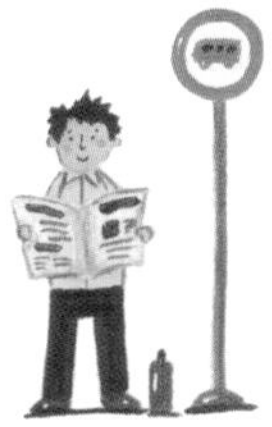

7

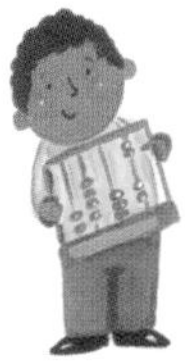

8

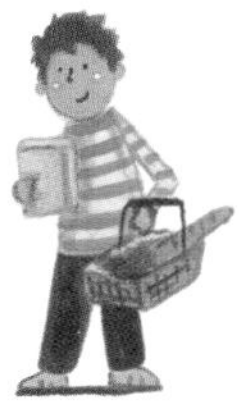

9

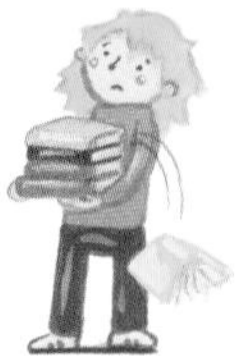

10

Take up the challenge!

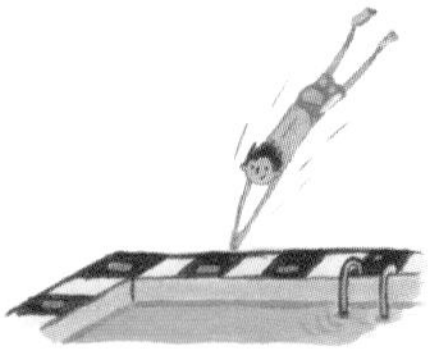

Complete the sentences in your book. Choose from these words.

(1 mark for each correct answer)

barked	howled	bellowed	trumpeted	hooted
roared	chattered	squeaked	bleated	croaked

1 The lamb ______.
2 The wolf ______.
3 The lion ______.
4 The monkey ____.
5 The bull ______.
6 The owl ______.
7 The mouse ____.
8 The frog ______.
9 The dog ______.
10 The elephant ____.

Adding –ing to verbs

🔑 Key idea

A verb is a doing word. You can add the suffix **–ing** to a verb. This changes the way you use it in a sentence.

The ships **sail**.   The ships are **sailing**.

Spelling rule 1

For verbs that end in **e**, you drop the e before adding **–ing**, like this: make = mak**ing**

Spelling rule 2

In one syllable words that have only one vowel before the final consonant, you double the consonant before adding **–ing**, like this:
ho**p** = ho**pping**

> **!**
> **ALERT**
> Here are some exceptions to the rule!
> galloping
> prohibiting

Try it out! •

Add –*ing* to these words. Remember the rules!

(1 mark for each correct answer)

shop	take	feel	dust	play
ride	skip	slip	slide	bake

Write the sentences and the missing words from the box. The start letter will help you. *(1 mark for each correct answer)*

going	hooting	hiding	using	getting
meeting	sitting	splashing	ringing	lifting

1 Mum was u_ _ _ _ the new mower to cut the grass.

2 Dan is g_ _ _ _ _ _ a new bike for his birthday.

3 Jenny is m_ _ _ _ _ _ Beth in town.

4 We are g_ _ _ _ to see the new film tonight.

5 Ben was h_ _ _ _ _ in the cupboard.

6 Jane is l_ _ _ _ _ _ the heavy bag out of the car.

7 The toddler is s_ _ _ _ _ _ in the paddling pool and
   s_ _ _ _ _ _ _ _ everyone!

8 The people in the parade were h_ _ _ _ _ _ horns
   and r_ _ _ _ _ _ bells.

Write a sentence using one of the words.

Write the words by the correct spelling rule in your book.

(1 mark for each correct answer)

running	biting	floating	digging	flying
swimming	hoping	walking	baking	stopping

1 Add –ing _____

2 Drop the e before adding –ing _____

3 Double the final consonant before adding –ing _____

Assessment 1

unit 8

Long vowel phonemes: ae and ee

Complete each of the words in your book by choosing the right letters from the box. *(1 mark for each correct answer)*

ae:	ai	a–e	ea	eigh	ay
ee:	ea	e–e	ee	ey	

1 br_ _ k   2 p_ _ l   3 _ _ _ _ t   4 b_ _ n   5 k_ _

Long vowel phonemes: ie, oe and ue

Complete these sentences in your book. Choose from the words in the box. *(1 mark for each correct answer)*

knight	note	boat	two	kite

1 The _____ is flying in the sky.
2 The big _____ has _____ masts.
3 The king wrote a _____ to the _____ .

Vowel phonemes: oo and ow

Sort these words under the right headings. *(1 mark for each correct answer)*

push	good	cow	bough	pull

oo	ow

Vowel phonemes: ar and oy

**Write the missing words to complete the sentences.
Choose from these words.** *(1 mark for each correct answer)*

> boil   boy   art   car   jar

1 A male child is called a _____.
2 You drive a _____ on the road.
3 You often draw pictures during an _____ lesson.
4 Jam is usually kept in a _____.
5 You _____ a kettle of water to make tea.

Plurals: adding s or es

Change these words into the plural. *(1 mark for each correct answer)*

solo _____   bat _____   banjo _____
ship _____   flower _____

Adding –ed

Put these words into the past tense by adding –ed. Remember the rules! *(0.5 mark for each correct answer)*

stop_____   kick_____   shop_____   call_____   hop_____

Adding –ing

Add –ing to these words. Remember the rules!
(0.5 mark for each correct answer)

skip_____   sit_____   fly_____   dance_____   jump_____

unit 9

Vowel phoneme: air

 Key idea

Some vowel phonemes can be tricky to spell. They may have three or more letters in their spelling pattern.

All these vowel phonemes say **air**.

Try it out! •

Read the clues below and choose the right *air* word from the box.

(1 mark for each correct answer)

mayor	hair	stairs	chair	pear
fair	hare	mare	bear	air

1 You climb up me to get to the next floor in a house.

2 I have long ears and look like a rabbit.

3 I have fur on me and I can growl loudly.

4 I am a female horse.

5 You sit on me to take a rest.

6 I grow on your head and you have to brush me to keep me looking smart.

7 You breathe me in.

8 I am a piece of fruit.

9 You can have fun here. There are lots of rides and side-shows.

10 I am an important person in the town. I have special robes and a chain of office to wear.

Choose the right word to complete these sentences.

(1 mark for each correct answer)

1 Mum bought a pear/pair of shoes.

2 You pay a fare/fair to travel on a bus.

3 You can usually find the mare/mayor at the town hall.

4 Mary and Meg were told to put on their/there coats.

5 It is rude to stare/stair at people.

6 Dad likes to where/wear his team scarf to football matches.

7 I opened the window to heir/air the room.

8 The pedlar sold his wares/wears at the market.

9 Dan paired/pared the apple with a fruit knife.

10 Amy didn't mean to tare/tear the book.

Take up the challenge! ●

Read the poem. Write a list of all the air words.
There are ten words to find. *(1 mark for each correct answer)*

Mary Dairy is a fairy
With wings as light as air
She's always doing magic
And flies almost anywhere.

She wears a pair of silver shoes
And has ribbons in her hair.
Her dress is made of rare French lace
And she sits in a golden chair.

unit
10

Vowel phonemes: or and er

🔑 **Key idea**

The vowel phonemes below say **or** or **er**. Most **er** vowel phonemes are formed with two or three letters, but some **or** vowel phonemes are formed with two, three or even four letters!

Read these **or** words. Can you hear the **or** sounds?

port	claws	caught
shore	bought	four

Now read these **er** words.
Can you hear the **er** sounds?

were	bird	birthday
disturbed	girl	crossword

 Top Tip

Remember that the word **bought** is the past tense of the verb **to buy!**

Try it out! •

Find and write the *or* and *er* words. The first one has been done for you. There are ten more to find. *(1 mark for each correct answer)*

1 When Pirate Pete arrived in *port*, he *bought* a toy ship.
2 The bird had sharp claws.
3 Jack was given four books for his birthday.
4 The girl caught a big fish.
5 There were many people on the shore.
6 Mum didn't want to be disturbed because she was doing a crossword.

Write the correct word for each picture. *(1 mark for each correct answer)*

1 claw/jaw   2 dawn/door   3 flaw/floor   4 bird/board

5 fort/fought   6 soar/saw   7 jaw/claw   8 word/world

9 fur/fir   10 curb/kerb

Take up the challenge! •

Make a chart like the one below. Write each of these words in the
correct column. *(1 mark for each correct answer)*

or	er

stalk   word   verb   cork   oar
taught   disturb   moor   whirred   further

21

Days of the week

🔑 **Key idea**

There are seven days in a week. Look carefully and you will see that all the names of all the days end in the word **day**. Read the poem.

> Monday's child is fair of face.
> Tuesday's child is full of grace.
> Wednesday's child is full of woe.
> Thursday's child has far to go.
> Friday's child is honest and giving.
> Saturday's child works hard for its living.
> And the child that is born on the Sabbath day
> Is bonny and blithe and good and gay.

 Top Tip

All the days of the week begin with a capital letter!

In this poem, the Sabbath day means Sunday!

Monday Tuesday Wednesday Thursday Friday Saturday Sunday

Try it out! •

Write the day of the week. *(1 mark for each correct answer)*

1 A child born on this day is full of woe.

2 A child born on this day works very hard to earn a living.

3 If you are born on this day you are good-looking.

22

4 A person born on this day will be graceful.

5 A child born today will have a long way to go.

6 If you are born on this day you will be an honest and giving person.

7 If you are born on this day you will be good-looking, cheerful and well-behaved.

8 Babies born on which two days have more than one characteristic?

Keep practising!

Unscramble the letters to make the days of the week.

(1 mark for each correct answer)

dyaSnu   Tdusyae   aStarduy

andoMy   ndesayWde   riFyad   urhTdyas

Take up the challenge!

Read the clue and write the day. *(1 mark for each correct answer)*

1 Which two days begin with the letter T?

2 Which three days have six letters in their names?

3 Which day comes after Monday?

4 Which day is three days after Friday?

5 What is the day before Saturday?

6 Which day is before Wednesday?

7 Which two days form the weekend?

8 Which day comes after Wednesday?

9 Which day is the first day of the school week?

10 Which days have eight letters in their names?

unit 12
Consonant digraphs: wh, ph and ch

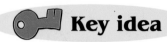 **Key idea**

Many words begin with the consonant digraphs **wh**, **ph** and **ch**.
Sometimes ph and ch can appear in the middle and at the end of
words. A consonant digraph is made up of two consonants that
make a single sound. Here are some examples.

where   **ph**antom   **wh**y   **ch**ip   **ph**armacy   **ch**alk

 Top Tip

wh words such as
what, when, where,
which, why, who
often begin questions.

 ALERT
ch can say **ch** as
in church or **c**
as in choir

Try it out! •

Write the words in your book. Circle the consonant digraphs in
each word. Be careful! Some words have more than one consonant
digraph. There are ten consonant digraphs to find. *(1 mark for each
correct consonant digraph)*

when	Philip	who	chase
church	echo	photograph	what

Keep practising!

Write *wh*, *ph* or *ch* to complete the words. Write the words in your book. *(1 mark for each correct answer)*

1 _ _ yllis is a girl's name.
2 _ _ illi is hot to eat!
3 An ele_ _ ant is a big animal
4 "_ _ at is the time?" asked Rahul.
5 Some people have mobile _ _ ones.
6 My sister is called _ _ ristine.
7 "_ _ ere is my coat?" asked Dad.
8 If you shout in a cave you may hear an e_ _ o.
9 My teacher asked _ _ o was my best friend.
10 We all like to sing in the school _ _ oir.

Take up the challenge!

Write the word. *(1 mark for each correct answer)*

1 elephant/elegant   2 chair/choir   3 while/wheel   4 phone/phrase

5 phantom/photograph   6 whistle/whip   7 chicken/chocolate

8 whip/whistle   9 chair/chain   10 cheese/chess

Compound words

 Key idea

A compound word is made up of two or more words that are joined together to make a new word. Here are some examples:

clipboard   paintbrush   lipstick   bookmark   pillowcase

 Top Tip

Remember to join the two words when you write a compound word. You must not leave a gap between them.

Try it out! ....

Read the clues on Pirate Pete's treasure map. Write down the compound words. There are ten to find. *(1 mark for each correct answer)*

Go to the playground.
Stop at the seesaw next to the roundabout.
Look right and you will see a farmhouse.
Walk through the farmyard.
Go past the broken gatepost and into the field.
Walk to the end and you will see a cliff with a waterfall.
  Stop there.
Turn round and take six steps to the right. Stop!
The treasure is hidden underground.
Dig a deep hole until you find the treasure chest.
Take the lid off and you will find the golden necklaces!

Find the missing words to complete the compound words. Write the compound words in your book. *(1 mark for each correct answer)*

boy	chair	cart	ear	mower
car	house	fly	round	barrow

1 Mum parked in the _____ port.

2 Ben was so excited he did a _____ wheel across the room.

3 Jasmine played on the _____ about.

4 Ravi's dad pushed the wheel _____ across the garden.

5 You keep plants in a green _____ to keep the frost off them.

6 You mow the grass with a lawn _____ .

7 Gran uses a wheel _____ because she cannot walk very well.

8 A butter _____ is a beautiful insect.

9 Sophie likes to wear sparkly _____ rings to parties.

10 Dan likes to dress up as a cow _____ .

Take up the challenge! •

Make two compound words from each root word. Choose the end words from the box. *(1 mark for each correct answer)*

bow	band	rest	ball	drop
card	path	chair	ache	code

1 rain   2 foot   3 post   4 arm   5 head

unit 14

Syllables

🔑 Key idea

Each beat in a word is called a syllable. Some words only have one syllable. These words are called monosyllabic words. But some words have more than one syllable. They are called multi-syllabic or polysyllabic words.

Say the words below.

  cat = 1 syllable   pirate = 2 syllables

⭐ **Top Tip**
Splitting a word into its syllables can help you to spell it accurately.

Try it out! ·

Read the words. Count the syllables in each word. Write down the number of syllables. *(1 mark for each correct answer)*

man	dinner	dinosaur
caterpillar	geography	happy
computer	spelling	syllable
polysyllabic		

Keep practising!

Write the names of the children in your book. Mark the syllable boundaries with a red pencil or felt-tip. *(1 mark for each correct answer)*

1 Mark 2 Hannah 3 Rahul 4 Dominic 5 Jonathan

6 Rebecca 7 Caroline 8 Rayhan 9 Natalie 10 Christina

Take up the challenge!

Copy the table below into your book. Write the animals under the correct heading. *(1 mark for each correct answer)*

hippopotamus   tiger   dog   mouse   giraffe

donkey   crocodile   elephant   alligator rhinoceros

1 syllable	2 syllables	3 syllables	4 syllables	5 syllables

Prefixes: un– and dis–

 ## Key idea

A prefix is a set of letters added to the start of a word. It changes the meaning of a word. Many prefixes are added to give words opposite meanings. **Un–** and **dis–** are called negative prefixes because they mean "not" or "opposite of".

sit!

sit!

obey

disobey

Here are some more examples.

unworn   uncertain   unhurt
unfair   unimportant   disappointed
disturbed   disappeared   disorder   disarm

> ⭐ **Top Tip**
>
> Remember the prefix rule! When you add a prefix you do not change the spelling of the root word.

> ! **ALERT**
>
> Look at these exceptions to the prefix rule:
> If you add 'all' or 'well' to words you remove an 'l':
> all + though = although
> well + fare = welfare

Try it out! •

Find the prefixed words. The first one has been done for you. There are ten more words to find. *(1 mark for each correct answer)*

1 The dog *disturbed* the flowerbed when it *unearthed* the bone.

2 Grandma was disappointed that the jumper was unworn.

3 The man was uncertain how to disarm the robber.

4 Lucy said it was unimportant that her room was in such disorder.

5 It was unfair that David disobeyed his teacher.

6 Gopal was unhurt apart from a small bruise that soon disappeared.

Keep practising! ●

Complete each sentence in your book. Choose from these words.

(1 mark for each correct answer)

> discontented   disbelieved   unlocked   untidy   unaware
> uncomfortable   unkind   disconnected   disliked displeased

1 Jacob's bedroom was always _____.

2 Dad _____ the door with his key.

3 She _____ Andrew's story because he rarely told the truth.

4 Mark liked jelly but _____ ice cream.

5 Jim _____ the television before going to bed.

6 It is mean to be _____ to people.

7 The sofa was _____ because of a loose spring.

8 Jodie was _____ of the dangers of swimming in the canal.

9 Ravinder felt _____ and bored on holiday.

10 Mum was _____ with Sam's bad behaviour.

Have you checked your spellings?

Take up the challenge! ●

Write *un–* or *dis–* in front of these words to make the opposite.

(1 mark for each correct answer)

1 ___certain   4 ___please   7 ___approve   9 ___harmed

2 ___respect   5 ___satisfy   8 ___agree   10 ___sure

3 ___lawful   6 ___clear

Assessment 2

Vowel phoneme: air

Choose the correct *air* word. *(1 mark for each correct answer)*

1 chair/care

2 fair/fare

3 pair/pear

4 bare/bear

5 hair/hare

6 mayor/mare

Vowel phonemes: or and er

Choose from these letters and complete the words below.

(1 mark for each correct answer)

| or | er | ir | ur | alk | ought |

c_ _n   b_ _d   f_ _   st_ _ _   f_ _n   th_ _ _ _ _

Days of the week

Write the days of the week in order. *(0.5 mark for each correct word and 0.5 mark for the correct order.)*

Consonant digraphs: wh, ph and ch

Choose the right word for each sentence. *(1 mark for each correct answer)*

1 "_____ is the time?" asked Ben. (When/What)

2 You take _____ with a camera. (phones/photographs)

3 You sit on a _____. (chair/cheese)

4 You can talk to someone on a _____. (phone/pharmacy)

5 "_____ are you going?" asked Mum. (Where/What)

Compound words

Join a word from the top box to one from the bottom box to make five compound words. *(1 mark for each correct answer)*

sauce	jig	butter	foot	shop

keeper	saw	ball	fly	pan

Syllables

Write the number of syllables in these words.

(1 mark for each correct answer)

1 supermarket   2 courtyard   3 mouse

4 computer   5 hippopotamus

Prefixes: un– and dis–

Add un– or dis– to the words below to make new words.

(1 mark for each correct answer)

1 agree   2 certain   3 sure   4 pleased   5 trust

Vowel phonemes: ear and ea

 Key idea

The vowel phoneme **ear** usually says "ear" as in **hear**. The vowel phoneme **ea** may say "e" as in **head**. There is no particular rule to help you spell words with these vowel phonemes, you have to try and remember them!

Read the **ear** and **ea** words.

hear here
dear deer
tear pier
peer

sped head
lead bread
breath bed

ALERT
Listen to the sound **ear** makes in these words.
pearl pear earn
Listen to the sound **ea** makes in these words.
peat feat pea

Try it out! •

Write the right word. *(1 mark for each correct answer)*

shed/sped

here/hear

dear/deer

bread/breath

peer/pier

head/lead

tread/thread

bed/bread

spread/spear

tear/tier

Read the definitions and write down the words that are being defined.
Choose from the words in the box. *(1 mark for each correct answer)*

> shed   wealthy   red   deaf   dear
> thread   sleepyhead   weir   pier   shortbread

1 A primary colour.

2 Someone who can't hear is this.

3 You are this if you have a lot of money.

4 This building is often found in a garden.

5 Another word for expensive.

6 You can walk along this at the seaside.

7 You sew with this.

8 A dam across a river.

9 A rich biscuit made with butter, flour and sugar.

10 You might be called this if you are very tired!

Take up the challenge! • • • • • • • • • • • • • • • • • •

Read the conversation between Mum and Fred.
Write down all the *ear* and *ea* words. There are ten words to find.
(1 mark for each correct answer)

"Wake up, sleepyhead," said Mum. "It's nearly time for school!"

"Can't I stay in bed instead?" moaned Fred. "I'm so tired."

"No, dear," replied Mum. "I can hear the school bus coming up the road. It's almost here." She gave his ear a tweak. "Come on, hurry up!"

Suffixes: –ful and –ly

Key idea

A suffix is a set of letters added to the end of a word, which changes the way it is used. This unit looks at the suffixes **–ful** and **–ly**.

wonder + ful = wonderful

clear + ly = clearly

happy + ly = happily

! ALERT

When you add a suffix to a word, sometimes the spelling of the root word changes.

Try it out! •

Read the story. Find and write the words with *–ful* and *–ly* suffixes. There are ten words to find. Be careful! One word has both suffixes. *(1 mark for each correct answer)*

It was a lovely day. The sun was shining brightly in the sky.

"What a wonderful day for my birthday," Emma said happily.

Dad was humming a cheerful tune while he set the table. Mum was quickly but carefully putting the finishing touches to Emma's birthday cake.

"It's such a beautiful cake," said Emma. "You are so skilful! Thank you, Mum."

Mum gave Emma a big hug. "I'm glad you like it," she said. "I'm just thankful I've finished it in time for your party!"

Write the most appropriate word to complete the sentences.
Choose from these words. *(1 mark for each correct answer)*

thankful	plentiful	lovely	clearly	truthful
dreadful	beautiful	lonely	lively	pitiful

1 A t＿＿＿＿＿＿ person never tells lies.

2 Jenny wore a b＿＿＿＿＿＿ dress.

3 Mary had a l＿＿＿＿＿＿ time at the seaside.

4 Rohan could see c＿＿＿＿＿＿ with his new glasses.

5 There was a d＿＿＿＿＿＿ thunderstorm last night.

6 The stray dog was in a p＿＿＿＿＿＿ state.

7 The school band played l＿＿＿＿＿＿ music.

8 John was l＿＿＿＿＿＿ because he had no friends.

9 Josh always seemed to have a p＿＿＿＿＿＿ supply of sweets.

10 Ayesha was t＿＿＿＿＿＿ for her mother's help.

Take up the challenge! •••••••••••••••••••••••••••

Put these words into sentences to show you understand their
meaning. You may use a dictionary to help you. *(1 mark for each
correct answer)*

1 sadly	2 hopeful	3 joyful	4 cleverly	5 awful
6 dutiful	7 boastful	8 spiteful	9 friendly	10 crossly

Numbers, months and colours

🔑 Key idea

There are important rules to remember when spelling months, numbers and colours. Months of the year are proper nouns and always begin with a capital letter.

January

April

July

September

> ⭐ **Top Tip**
> There are twelve months in a year.

Numbers and colours are adjectives and never begin with a capital letter unless they appear at the beginning of a sentence!

Here are some number words:

   eight   three   fifteen   ten

Here are some colour words:

   white   purple   red   green

Try it out! •••••••••••••••••••••••••••••••••••

Find the months, numbers or colours in these sentences. The first one has been done for you. There are ten more to find. *(1 mark for each correct answer)*

1 In July, Jack went on holiday for ten days. *(July, ten)*

2 Mary had three red jumpers.

3 Jason wore a new green uniform when he started school in September.

4 In January, it snowed hard and everywhere was white.

5 Dan gave eight purple marbles to Gopal.

6 In April, fifteen lambs were born on the farm.

Keep practising! ··························

Read the clues. Write a month, colour or number word.
Choose from these words. *(1 mark for each correct answer)*

June	pink	one	blue	ten
August	eleven	yellow	December	orange

1 This month comes between July and September.
2 You make this colour by mixing red and white.
3 You get this number if you add five and six together.
4 This is the last month of the year.
5 The sky is often this colour.
6 The first number.
7 This colour is also the name of a fruit.
8 The sixth month of the year.
9 The sum of two and eight.
10 Bananas are usually this colour.

Take up the challenge! ·····················

Draw and label these things. *(1 mark for each correct label and picture)*

1 three blue candles
2 six black cats
3 twenty red sweets
4 nine pink cakes
5 sixteen white snowballs

6 twelve purple hats
7 fourteen yellow flowers
8 seventeen green caterpillars
9 thirteen orange balloons
10 eighteen brown buttons

unit 20

Vowel phoneme: o (or "w" special)

🔑 Key idea

In some words the letter "a" says **o**. This often happens when the "a" comes after w, wh, sw, qu or squ.

*I will **wash** my clothes in the **washing**-machine.*

squashed   was   want   what   watch

Read the words on the washing line. Can you hear the **o** sound?

Try it out! •

Read the story. Find and write down in your book all the *o* words. There are ten to find. *(1 mark for each correct answer)*

Pirate Pete was busy doing his washing. He didn't want to wash his clothes but they were very dirty!

First of all he squashed all the clothes into the sink. Next he poured in some soap powder and added some water.

He scrubbed the clothes on an old washboard.

"What a tiring job!" he sighed. "I wish I could wave a magic wand and make the clothes clean."

Soon the clothes were nice and clean. Pete hung them up on the line to dry.

"I'd better watch out for rain," he said. But luckily there wasn't any rain all afternoon.

Keep practising!

Read the dictionary definitions. Write the correct headword for each definition. Choose from the words in the box below. You may use a dictionary to help you. *(1 mark for each correct answer)*

swallow	· quarrel	quarry	quantity	watt
watchdog	quaff	swamp	squander	swab

1 to drink deeply
2 a bird with a forked tail
3 an argument
4 a dog that guards property or people
5 to spend money wastefully

6 a marshy place
7 a place from which stone and rock are taken
8 to mop up
9 the size or amount of something
10 a unit of power

Take up the challenge!

Write the word. *(2 marks for each correct answer)*

quadruplets/quadrangles

watchdog/washroom

wallaby/waffle

watchful/watchman

swabbing/swaddling

Revising long vowel phonemes

🔑 Key idea

Do you remember that at the start of this book we looked at long vowel sounds? Two or more vowels in a word *usually* make a long vowel sound.

> ⭐ **Top Tip**
>
> When two vowels go walking the first does the talking – so **ai** says **ay**!

Read the words. Can you hear the long vowel sounds?

Try it out! ●

Look at the pictures. Write the word in your book.

(1 mark for each correct answer)

1

2

3

4

5

6

7

8

9

10

Write the word that completes the sentence.

(1 mark for each correct answer)

1 The fire burned in the _____. (great/grate)

2 The king sat on a golden _____. (throne/thrown)

3 Bats come out at _____. (night/knight)

4 Jack had a hole in the _____ of his shoe. (soul/sole)

5 The car sped along the _____. (rode/road)

6 You make bread from _____. (dough/doe)

7 Everyone left the beach when the _____ turned. (tide/tied)

8 We climbed over the _____ to get into the field. (style/stile)

9 A horse has a long _____. (tail/tale)

10 The _____ was covered in pebbles. (beech/beach)

Copy the table below into your book. Write the words under the correct sound. *(1 mark for each correct answer)*

tune	hope	I	beat	these
cake	shoe	play	eye	pillow

ae	ee	ie	oe	ue

Assessment 3

Vowel phonemes: ear and ea

Write the *ear* or *ea* word. *(0.5 mark for each correct answer)*

1   2   3   4

5   6   7   8

Suffixes: –ful and –ly

Add *–ful* or *–ly* to these words to make new words.
(0.5 mark for each correct answer)

lone_____   beauty_____   thank_____   pity_____   love_____
sad_____   care_____   loud_____   kind_____   awe_____

Numbers, months and colours

Write the number, month or colour. *(0.5 mark for each correct answer)*

1 The month after May.
2 The colour of grass.
3 The colour of the sun.
4 The number before five.
5 The month before November.
6 The colour of the sky.
7 The third month of the year.
8 Three plus six.
9 Ten minus four.
10 The colour of coal.

Vowel phoneme: o (or "w" special)

Write the headword for each of these dictionary definitions. Each headword is an _o_ ("w" special) word. *(1 mark for each correct answer)*

1 To clean with soap and water. (4 letters)
2 To argue. (8 letters)
3 To crush something. (6 letters)
4 A duck moves like this. (6 letters)
5 A large white bird with long neck. (4 letters)
6 A magician uses one of these. (4 letters)
7 A place from which rock and stone is taken. (6 letters)
8 Four children born at the same time to the same mother. (11 letters)
9 This insect can sting you. (4 letters)
10 An animal that looks like a small kangaroo. (7 letters)

Revising long vowel phonemes

Choose a long vowel phoneme word to complete each sentence. Write the word in your book. *(0.5 mark for each correct answer)*

1 The _____ shines at night. (moon/moan)
2 You wear a _____ to keep you warm. (coal/coat)
3 A _____ is a musical instrument. (flume/flute)
4 _____ is a colour. (Blue/Blew)
5 You _____ with a pen or pencil. (write/right)
6 It is fun to _____ with your friends. (pay/play)
7 A _____ runs along a railway track. (drain/train)
8 A _____ is a type of tree. (beech/beach)
9 A bird can fly up in the _____. (sty/sky)
10 You wear _____ on your feet. (booms/boots)

Have you checked your spellings?

Word lists

Page 2   be   bean   bee   cape   day   eight   great   meat   pail   sea   tape   theme   whale

Page 3   bean   bee   brake   break   cake   made   maid   pail   scene   seen   sheep   way   weak   week   weigh   whale   whey

Page 4   blue   dough   fight   fly   hide   I   moon   only   sky   so   to   toe   use   view   window   writes   yellow

Page 5   blew   blow   blue   boot   cry   road   rode   role   roll   sight   site   so   sow   write

Page 6   around   bough   good   growled   house   looked   mouse   now   out   push   put   stood   took   would

Page 7   book   bough   bow   count   cowboy   eyebrow   farmhouse   greenhouse   hood   hook   mouse   pound   pull   push   town   wood   would

Page 8   ahoy   arm   boy   buoy   car   chart   coins   dart   guitar   loyal   market   oil   palm   royal   shark   soil

Page 9   alarm   annoy   art   boil   boy   card   cart   dark   jar   loyal   march   marmalade   oil   royal

Page 10   bags   balloons   banjos   boys   cars   echoes   eskimos   flamingoes   flamingos   igloos   logos   pianos   potatoes   rats   ship   ships   solos   tomatoes

Page 11   boys   buoys   cars   cups   flours   flowers   footballs   hats   jars   knights   monkeys   moons   nights   pens   planks   plants   sails   sales   schools   sweets

Page 12   call   cross   dim   dimmed   dip   dipped   hop   hopped   jump   jumped   lock   look   need   play   pull   push   stop   stopped   walk   want

Page 13   barked   bellowed   bleated   chased   chattered   counted   cracked   croaked   danced   dived   dropped   hooted   howled   kicked   roared   shopped   squeaked   trumpeted   waited

Page 14   bake   dust   feel   galloping   hop   hopping   make   making   play   prohibiting   ride   sail   sailing   shop   skip   slide   slip   take

Page 15   baking   biting   digging   floating   flying   getting   going   hiding   hooting   hoping   lifting   meeting   ringing   running   sitting   splashing   stopping   swimming   using   walking

Page 16   bean   boat   bough   break   cow   eight   good   key   kite   knight   note   pail   pull   push   two

Page 17   art   banjo   bat   boil   boy   call   car   dance   flower   fly   hop   jar   jump   kick   ship   shop   sit   skip   solo   stop

Page 18   air   bear   chair   fair   hair   hare   mare   mayor   pear   stairs

Page 19   air   anywhere   chair   dairy   fair   fairy   fare   hair   heir   mare   Mary   mayor   pair   paired   pared   pear   rare   stair   stare   tare   tear   their   there   wares   wear   wears   where

Page 20   bird   birthday   bought   caught   claws   crossword   disturbed   four   girl   port   shore   were

Page 21   bird   board   claw   cork   curb   dawn   disturb   door   fir   flaw   floor   fort   fought   fur   further   jaw   kerb   moor   oar   saw   soar   stalk   taught   verb   whirred   word   world

Page 22   Friday   Monday   Sabbath   Saturday   Sunday   Thursday   Tuesday   Wednesday

Page 23   Friday   Monday   Sabbath   Saturday   Sunday   Thursday   Tuesday   Wednesday

Page 24   chalk   chase   chip   choir   church   echo   phantom   pharmacy   Philip   photograph   what   when   where   which   who   why

Page 25   chain   chair   cheese   chess   chicken   chilli   chocolate   choir   Christine   echo   elegant   elephant   phantom   phone   phones   photograph   phrase   Phyllis   what   wheel   where   while   whip   whistle   who

Page 26   bookmark   clipboard   farmhouse   farmyard   gatepost   into   lipstick   necklaces   paintbrush   pillowcase   playground   roundabout   seesaw   underground   waterfall

Page 27   armband   armchair   armrest   barrow   boy   butterfly   car   carport   cart   cartwheel   chair   cowboy   ear   earrings   fly   football   footpath   greenhouse   headache   headband   headrest   house   lawnmower   mower   postcard   postcode   rainbow   raindrop   round   roundabout   wheelbarrow   wheelchair

Page 28   cat   caterpillar   computer   dinner   dinosaur   geography   happy   man   pirate   polysyllabic   spelling   syllable

Page 29   alligator   Caroline   Christina   crocodile   dog   Dominic   donkey   elephant   giraffe   Hannah   hippopotamus   Jonathan   Mark   mouse   Natalie   Rahul   Rayhan   Rebecca   rhinoceros   tiger

Page 30   although   disappeared   disappointed   disarm   disobey   disorder   disturbed   obey   uncertain   unearthed   unfair   unhurt   unimportant   unworn   welfare

Page 31   agree   approve   certain   clear   disappeared   disbelieved   disconnected   discontented   disliked   disobeyed   displeased   harmed   lawful   please   respect   satisfy   sure   unaware   uncomfortable   unfair   unhurt   unkind   unlocked   untidy

Page 32 bare bear bird care chair corn fair fare fern fur hair hare mare mayor pair pear stalk thought

Page 33 agree ball butter certain chair cheese computer courtyard fly foot green hippopotamus jig keeper mouse pan pharmacy phone phones photographs pleased sauce saw shop supermarket sure trust what when where

Page 34 bed bread breath dear deer earn feat head hear here lead pea pear pearl peat peer pier shed spear sped spread tear thread tier tread

Page 35 bed deaf dear ear Fred hear here instead nearly pier red said shed shortbread sleepyhead thread wealthy weir

Page 36 beautiful brightly carefully cheerful clearly happily lovely quickly skilful thankful wonderful

Page 37 awful beautiful boastful clearly cleverly crossly dreadful dutiful friendly hopeful joyful lively lonely lovely pitiful plentiful sadly spiteful thankful truthful

Page 38 April eight fifteen green January July purple red September ten three white

Page 39 April August black blue brown December eight eighteen eleven fifteen fourteen green January June nine one orange pink purple red seventeen six sixteen ten thirteen three twelve twenty white yellow

Page 40 squashed wand want was wash washboard washing washing-machine wasn't watch what

Page 41 quadrangles quadruplets quaff quantity quarrel quarry squander swab swabbing swaddling swallow swamp waffle wallaby washroom watchdog watchful watchman watt

Page 42 bike boat boy clown fly moon sheep spoon train whale

Page 43 beach beat beech cake doe dough eye grate great hope I knight night pillow play road rode shoe sole soul stile style tail tale these throne thrown tide tied tune

Page 44 awe beauty bread core deer ear head kind lone loud love pier pity sad shed tear thank thread

Page 45 beach beech blew blue booms boots coal coat drain flume flute moan moon pay play right sky sty train write